I ♥ POO!

An Odd Squad book for POO LOVERS everywhere!
by Allan Plenderleith

ЯR
RAVETTE PUBLISHING

**THE ODD SQUAD and all related characters © 2005
Created by Allan Plenderleith**

First Published by
Ravette Publishing Limited 2005
PO Box 876, Horsham
West Sussex, RH12 9GH

Reprinted 2006 (twice), 2007, 2009, 2010, 2011, 2012, 2016

ISBN: 978-1-84161-394-9

From his angle, Jeff was mistakenly convinced his clever dog could do a handstand.

Judging by all the 'chocolate kisses' on the floor
the dog's bum was in need of a wash again.

If you're going to poo outside, remember to pull your g-string down first.

Unable to flush her huge poo down her host's toilet, Maude simply hides it in her handbag.

Unfortunately, when Maude had said she wanted Jeff to do something kinky in bed, he had misheard.

Never blow off in the doggy position.

Dug had eaten one too many curly wurlies.

At the barber's, Jeff asked for a 'Number Two'.

Mid-poo, Billy's toilet paper ran out.

The Odd Squad Guide to

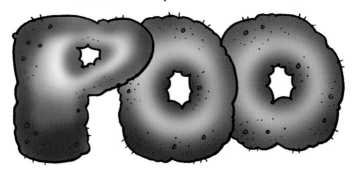

'THE FIREBALL'

HOT AND PAINFUL.
MAY SINGE
BOTTOM HAIRS.

'THE CHOP OFF'

POO IS STOPPED
HALF-WAY DUE TO
PHONE RINGING ETC.

'THE STICKY'

STICKS TO HAIRS.
REQUIRES HOURS OF
WIPING.

'THE VEGGIE'

LOOKS AND SMELLS
EXACTLY LIKE A
VEGGIE BURGER.

'THE FIREHOSE'

MAINLY WATER-BASED.
CREATES HUGE MESS.

'THE CROQUETTES'

CRISPY ON THE OUTSIDE
WITH A LIGHT, PUFFY
CENTRE.

'THE SLIPPY'

SLIPS OUT IN ONE, SWIFT MOVEMENT. REQUIRES NO WIPING.

"THE STINKER"

REEKS SO BAD YOU DON'T EVEN RECOGNISE THE SMELL.

'THE BLIP'

SMALL BUT CAUSES BIG SPLASH.

'THE NEVERENDING STORY'

AN AMAZING ACHIEVEMENT. MAY NEED TO STAND TO ACCOMPLISH FULL LENGTH.

'THE SWEETCORN'
MOST COLOURFUL
AND ATTRACTIVE.

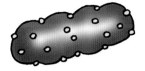

'THE JAGGY'
CAUSED BY EATING
TOO MANY CRISPS.
MAY RESULT IN
SURGERY.

'THE POPPETS'
COME OUT LIKE MACHINE
GUN BULLETS.

'THE STEAMY HEAPY'
WILL NEVER FLUSH.

THE CHINESE MEAL POO

NICE AT THE TIME BUT ULTIMATELY UNSATISFYING. YOU'LL FEEL LIKE ANOTHER ONE IN HALF AN HOUR.

THE McBURGER POO

DRY, OVERCOOKED, AND EACH POO IS IDENTICAL . WARNING: MAY CONTAIN TEENAGE STAFF'S BOGIES!

THE INDIAN MEAL POO

A REAL ARSE BURNER. SITTING DOWN
WILL BE IMPOSSIBLE FOR WEEKS.
KEEP FIRE EXTINGUISHER HANDY.

THE FISH + CHIPS POO

A SUCCULENT POO WITH A CRISPY OUTER COATING. FOLLOWED BY A SIDE PORTION OF MUSHY PEE POO!

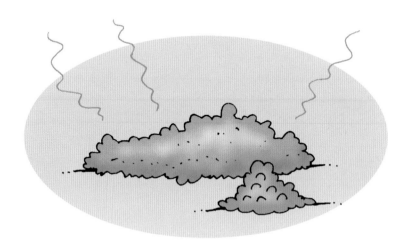

Once again, the dog had swallowed the
icing bag nozzle.

Never blow off in a g-string.

Billy impressed his friends with
his very own 'poo bear'.

If her date's shadow was anything to go by,
this was going to be one hell of a night!

Jeff walked into the garden to find it
full of toad stools.

Jeff enters another
'wipe it or leave it' dilemma.

TOP 5 THINGS
that have happened to everyone in the TOILET!

1. The Disappearing Poo!

It's always a big one, but when you look round it's gone!! No-one can explain this frustrating mystery.

Where is it?! I'm SURE I did one!

2. Splashback!

Occurs with small poos.
They create a huge splash
covering you in toilet water.
Most unpleasant.

3. The Unflushable Poo!

Does not budge after repeated flushings.

Options:

1. Chop it with a knife
2. Fish it out with tongs and dispose safely.

OR   3. Live with it.

4. The Reluctant Poo!

The poo that comes out half way and stops. Only option is to slice in half with sphincter.

5. The Neverending Wipe!

You keep on wiping but
you NEVER get clean!
You may be there for days.
(World Record stands at 7 years)

Over the years, Jeff had learned to read
the dog's mind.

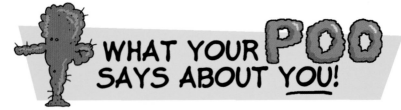

WHAT YOUR POO SAYS ABOUT YOU!

1.

YOU'RE A VERY GENEROUS, GIVING PERSON.
ALTHOUGH YOU GIVE SO MUCH IT LEAVES
YOU FEELING EMPTY INSIDE.

2.

A MESSY AND
IMPULSIVE PERSON.
WHEN YOU DECIDE TO
DO SOMETHING YOU
DROP EVERYTHING
AND GO!

3.

A SADO-MASOCHIST! YOU ENJOY PAIN
BUT YOU DO HAVE A TENDER SIDE.
(IE. YOUR TENDER BACKSIDE!)

4.

A REAL SNAKE IN THE GRASS!
YOU'RE A SLIPPERY CUSTOMER
WHO LIKES TO LEAVE NASTY
SURPRISES IN LONG GRASS!

5.  YOU NEVER FINISH ANYTHING, ALWAYS CUTTING OFF JOBS HALF WAY THROUGH!

6.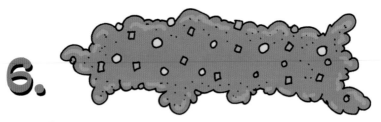

YOU'RE A VERY COLOURFUL PERSON WITH A CORNY SENSE OF HUMOUR!

7. STINGY GIT.

8.

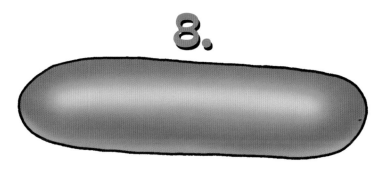

YOU'RE A VERY NEAT PERSON WHO NEVER LEAVES ANY MESS. BUT YOU'RE ALSO SLIGHTLY BORING.

9.

COLD AND EVIL WITH A HEART OF STONE. YOU LIKE TO HURT SMALL ANIMALS.

Jeff plays that popular party game
'Guess the REAL walnut whip!'

HOW YOUR POOS CHANGE AS YOU GET OLDER!

BABY POO
LIKE NUCLEAR CABBAGE ONLY MORE DEADLY. DO NOT LET IT COME IN CONTACT WITH YOUR SKIN.

TEENAGE POO
JUST A BIG BALL OF LARD, MADE FROM A DIET OF BURGERS, PIZZAS & CHOCOLATE. HIGHLY INFECTIOUS.

TWENTYSOMETHING POO

POO IS GREEN DUE TO SUDDEN HEALTH KICK. BUT MORE VEG IN DIET MEANS SMELLIER POOS.

THIRTYSOMETHING POO

INCREASE IN DINNER PARTIES MEANS POOS BECOME DARKER AND RICHER IN QUALITY. THE BOUQUET IS ALMOST PLEASANT.

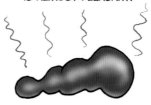

FORTYSOMETHING POO

MIDDLE AGE SPREAD SETS IN. POOS BECOME HUGE SWOLLEN MONSTROSITIES, JUST LIKE THEIR BIG ARSES.

OLD AGED POO (O.A.P.)

POOS ARE GREY, WRINKLY, DRIED UP AND SMELL LIKE ROTTING FLESH. JUST LIKE AN OLD PERSON REALLY!

Maude was about to say how nice the new jacuzzi was, when she noticed something.

Other ODD SQUAD hardback gift books available ...

		ISBN	Price
Jeff's Dog - Diary of a bad dog	**(new)**	978-1-84161-386-4	£5.99
The Odd Squad's Kama Sutra	**(new)**	978-1-84161-385-7	£5.99
Cartoons to Cheer up a Grumpy Old Git		978-1-84161-360-4	£4.99
Cartoons to Cheer up a Stroppy Mare		978-1-84161-361-1	£4.99
I Love Beer		978-1-84161-238-6	£5.99
I Love Dad		978-1-84161-395-6	£5.99
I Love Mum		978-1-84161-249-2	£5.99
I Love Sex		978-1-84161-241-6	£4.99
I Love Wine		978-1-84161-239-3	£4.99
I Love Xmas		978-1-84161-262-1	£4.99

HOW TO ORDER:

Please send a cheque/postal order in £ sterling, made payable to 'Ravette Publishing'
for the cover price of the book/s and allow the following for post & packing ...

UK & BFPO	70p for the first book & 40p per book thereafter
Europe & Eire	£1.30 for the first book & 70p per book thereafter
Rest of the world	£2.20 for the first book & £1.10 per book thereafter

RAVETTE PUBLISHING LTD
PO Box 876, Horsham, West Sussex   RH12 9GH
Tel: 01403 711443   Fax: 01403 711554   Email: info@ravettepub.co.uk
www.ravettepublishing.tel

Prices and availability are subject to change without prior notice